JULIUS CAESAR

ILLUSTRATED BY

MUSTASHRIK

Published by
SelfMadeHero
A division of Metro Media Ltd
5 Upper Wimpole Street
London W1G 6BP
www.selfmadehero.com

This edition published 2008

Illustrator: Mustashrik
Text Adaptor: Richard Appignanesi
Designer: Andy Huckle
Cover Colourist: Robert Deas
Textual Consultant: Nick de Somogyi
Publisher: Emma Hayley

ISBN: 978-0-9552856-5-3

10 9 8 7 6 5 4 3 2 1
Printed and bound in China

Julius Caesar, a military hero, risks assassination if he claims dictatorship of a republic destabilized by recent civil war.
Julius Caesar
"I am constant as the northern star..."
"Beware the Ides of March!"
A soothsayer

The seeds of resistance to Caesar's dictatorship
"I know that virtue
to be in you, Brutus."
Cassius, arch enemy of Caesar
"I love the name of
honour more than
I fear death."
Brutus, defender of the republic

"I do fear the people choose Caesar for their king."
"And why should Caesar be a tyrant then?"

Conspirators allied to Brutus and Cassius
"I will set this foot of mine as far as who goes farthest."
Cinna
"Liberty! Freedom! Tyranny is dead!"
Casca
"Stand fast together!"
Metellus Cimber

Trebonius
"Men, wives and children run as it were doomsday."
"It sufficeth that Brutus leads me…"
Ligarius
"Shall no man else be touched but Caesar?"
Decius

"You shall not stir out
of your house today."
"Yet Caesar shall
go forth..."
Caesar
Calpurnia, wife of Caesar

"You have some sick offence within your mind..."
Portia, wife of Brutus
Brutus
"O ye gods, render me worthy of this noble wife!"

The avengers of Caesar's murder
"Over thy wounds now do I prophesy
– fury and fierce civil strife!"
Mark Antony, loyal friend of Caesar

"I draw a sword till Caesar's three-and-thirty wounds be well avenged!"
Octavius, nephew and adopted son of Julius Caesar

THE PEOPLE OF ROME CELEBRATE JULIUS CAESAR'S TRIUMPH OVER HIS RIVAL, POMPEY. BUT SOME LOYAL REPUBLICANS FEAR CAESAR'S AMBITION...
WE LOVE
IS THIS A HOLIDAY?
INDEED, SIR, WE MAKE HOLIDAY TO SEE CAESAR, AND REJOICE IN HIS TRIUMPH.
KNEW YOU NOT POMPEY?
AND YOU NOW STREW FLOWERS IN HIS WAY THAT COMES IN TRIUMPH OVER POMPEY'S BLOOD?
BE GONE!

LET NO IMAGES BE HUNG WITH CAESAR'S TROPHIES – WHO WOULD KEEP US ALL IN SERVILE FEARFULNESS!

JULIUS CAESAR RECEIVES A PROPHETIC WARNING...
I HEAR A TONGUE, SHRILLER THAN ALL THE MUSIC, CRY "CAESAR!"
BEWARE THE IDES OF MARCH!
A SOOTHSAYER BIDS YOU BEWARE THE IDES OF MARCH.

HE IS
A DREAMER.
LET US LEAVE
HIM.
BRUTUS,
I DO OBSERVE YOU
NOW OF LATE.
YOU BEAR
TOO STRANGE A HAND
OVER YOUR FRIEND
THAT LOVES YOU.

CASSIUS, BE NOT DECEIVED.
I TURN THE TROUBLE OF MY COUNTENANCE MERELY UPON MYSELF.
POOR BRUTUS, WITH HIMSELF AT WAR, FORGETS THE SHOWS OF LOVE TO OTHER MEN.
CAESAR RULES
LIVE

TELL ME, BRUTUS,
CAN YOU SEE YOUR FACE?
NO, CASSIUS,
FOR THE EYE SEES
NOT ITSELF.
MANY OF THE BEST IN ROME,
GROANING UNDERNEATH THIS AGE'S
YOKE, HAVE WISHED THAT NOBLE
BRUTUS HAD HIS EYES.
INTO WHAT DANGERS
WOULD YOU LEAD ME,
CASSIUS?

I, YOUR GLASS, WILL MODESTLY DISCOVER TO YOURSELF THAT OF YOURSELF WHICH YOU YET KNOW NOT OF.
WHAT MEANS THIS SHOUTING? I DO FEAR THE PEOPLE CHOOSE CAESAR FOR THEIR KING.
AY, DO YOU FEAR IT? THEN MUST I THINK YOU WOULD NOT HAVE IT SO.

I WOULD NOT, CASSIUS, YET I LOVE HIM WELL.
BUT I LOVE THE NAME OF HONOUR MORE THAN I FEAR DEATH.
I KNOW THAT VIRTUE TO BE IN YOU, BRUTUS.
I WAS BORN FREE AS CAESAR. SO WERE YOU.
WE CAN BOTH ENDURE THE WINTER'S COLD AS WELL AS HE.

ONCE, UPON A RAW AND GUSTY DAY, CAESAR SAID TO ME...
"DAR'ST THOU, CASSIUS, NOW LEAP IN WITH ME INTO THIS ANGRY FLOOD?"
I PLUNGED IN AND BADE HIM FOLLOW.
BUT ERE WE COULD ARRIVE THE POINT PROPOSED, CAESAR CRIED...

"HELP ME, CASSIUS, OR I SINK!"
SO FROM THE WAVES OF TIBER DID I BEAR THE TIRED CAESAR.
AND THIS MAN IS NOW BECOME A GOD.
IT DOTH AMAZE ME, A MAN OF SUCH A FEEBLE TEMPER SHOULD BEAR THE PALM ALONE.

ANOTHER GENERAL SHOUT?
I DO BELIEVE THAT THESE APPLAUSES ARE FOR SOME NEW HONOURS HEAPED ON CAESAR.
HE DOTH BESTRIDE THE NARROW WORLD LIKE A COLOSSUS.
"CAESAR?" WHY SHOULD THAT NAME BE SOUNDED MORE THAN YOURS?
UPON WHAT MEAT DOTH CAESAR FEED THAT HE IS GROWN SO GREAT?
ROME, THOU HAST LOST THE BREED OF NOBLE BLOODS!

WHAT YOU HAVE SAID I WILL CONSIDER...
TILL THEN, MY NOBLE FRIEND, CHEW UPON THIS —
BRUTUS HAD RATHER BE A VILLAGER THAN TO REPUTE HIMSELF A SON OF ROME UNDER THESE HARD CONDITIONS AS THIS TIME IS LIKE TO LAY UPON US.
I AM GLAD MY WEAK WORDS HAVE STRUCK THUS MUCH FIRE FROM BRUTUS.

CAESAR AND ANTONY OBSERVE CASSIUS...
LET ME HAVE MEN ABOUT ME THAT ARE FAT.
CASSIUS HAS A LEAN AND HUNGRY LOOK.
HE THINKS TOO MUCH. SUCH MEN ARE DANGEROUS.
FEAR HIM NOT, CAESAR, HE'S NOT DANGEROUS.
HE IS A NOBLE ROMAN, AND WELL GIVEN.

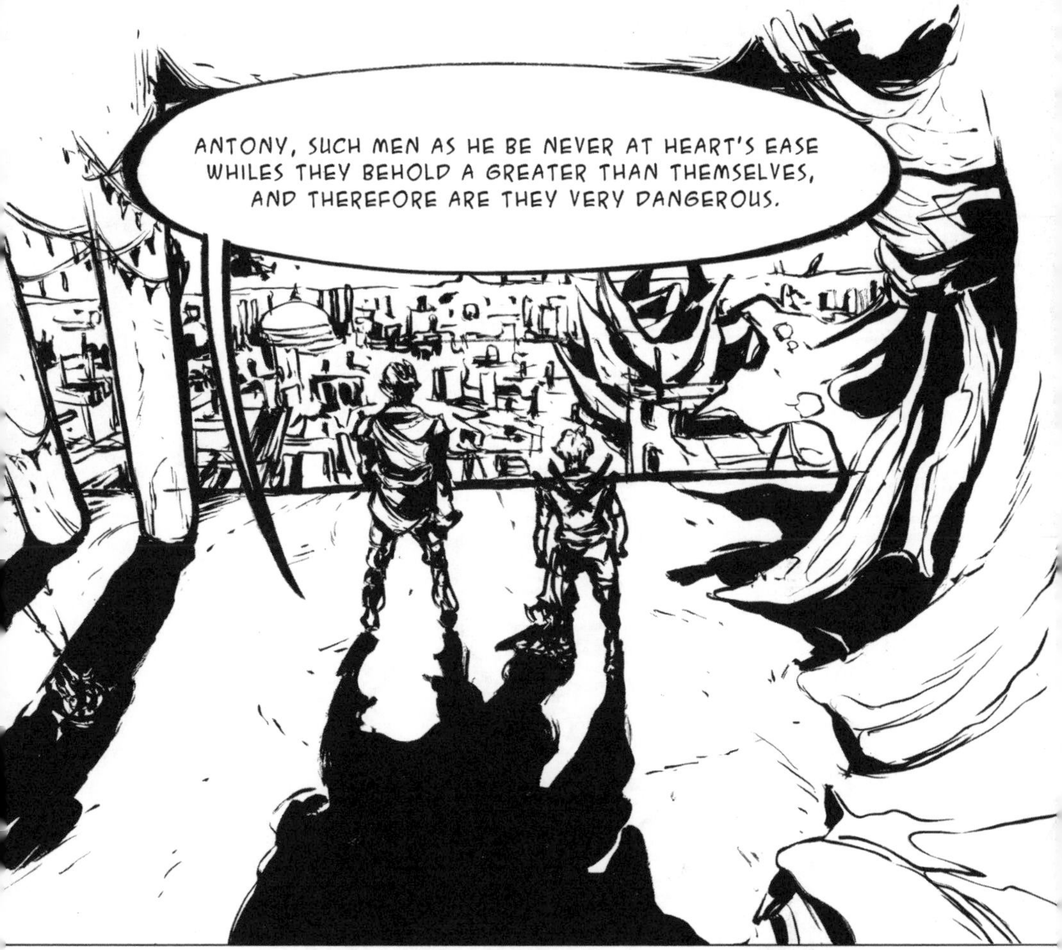

ANTONY, SUCH MEN AS HE BE NEVER AT HEART'S EASE
WHILES THEY BEHOLD A GREATER THAN THEMSELVES,
AND THEREFORE ARE THEY VERY DANGEROUS.

CASCA REPORTS ON THE NEWS FROM THE MARKET-PLACE.
CASCA, TELL US WHAT HATH CHANCED TODAY THAT CAESAR LOOKS SO SAD.
WHY, THERE WAS A CROWN OFFERED HIM, AND HE PUT IT BY WITH THE BACK OF HIS HAND, THUS.
AND THEN THE PEOPLE FELL A-SHOUTING.
WHO OFFERED HIM THE CROWN?
WHY, ANTONY.

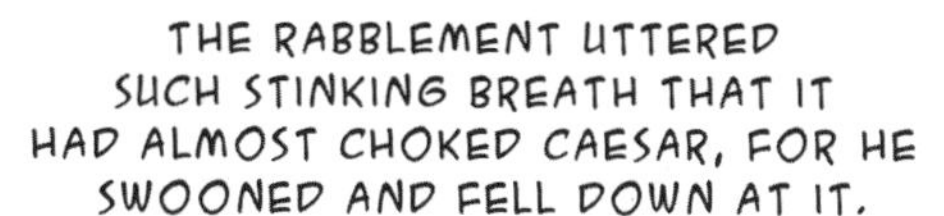
THE RABBLEMENT UTTERED SUCH STINKING BREATH THAT IT HAD ALMOST CHOKED CAESAR, FOR HE SWOONED AND FELL DOWN AT IT.
WHAT!
DID CAESAR SWOON?
HE FELL DOWN AND FOAMED AT MOUTH.
'TIS VERY LIKE: HE HATH THE FALLING-SICKNESS.

WHAT SAID HE, WHEN HE CAME UNTO HIMSELF?
HE SAID, IF HE HAD DONE OR SAID ANYTHING AMISS...
HE DESIRED THEIR WORSHIPS TO THINK IT WAS HIS INFIRMITY.
THREE OR FOUR WENCHES CRIED,
"ALAS! GOOD SOUL!"
IF CAESAR HAD STABBED THEIR MOTHERS, THEY WOULD HAVE DONE NO LESS.

WILL YOU DINE
WITH ME TOMORROW?
AY,
IF I BE ALIVE.
WHAT A BLUNT FELLOW
IS THIS GROWN TO BE!
SO IS HE NOW, IN
EXECUTION OF ANY
BOLD OR NOBLE
ENTERPRISE.
TOMORROW, IF YOU PLEASE
TO SPEAK WITH ME,
I WILL WAIT FOR YOU.

I WILL DO SO.
TILL THEN, THINK OF THE WORLD.
WELL, BRUTUS, THOU ART NOBLE.
YET I SEE THY HONOURABLE METAL MAY BE WROUGHT FROM THAT IT IS DISPOSED.
FOR WHO SO FIRM THAT CANNOT BE SEDUCED?

CAESAR DOTH BEAR ME HARD;
BUT HE LOVES BRUTUS.
I WILL THIS NIGHT AT HIS WINDOWS THROW WRITINGS, ALL TENDING TO THE GREAT OPINION THAT ROME HOLDS OF HIS NAME.
AND AFTER THIS LET CAESAR SEAT HIM SURE — FOR WE WILL SHAKE HIM OR WORSE DAYS ENDURE.

IN A STORM THAT NIGHT, CASCA MEETS THE SENATOR CICERO.
CASCA, WHY ARE YOU BREATHLESS?
O CICERO!
NEVER TILL TONIGHT DID I GO THROUGH A TEMPEST DROPPING FIRE.
A COMMON SLAVE HELD UP HIS LEFT HAND, WHICH DID FLAME AND BURN, AND YET REMAINED UNSCORCHED.

I MET A LION WHO GLARED UPON ME,
AND WENT SURLY BY WITHOUT ANNOYING ME.
A HUNDRED GHASTLY WOMEN
SWORE THEY SAW MEN, ALL IN FIRE,
WALK UP AND DOWN THE STREETS.

AND YESTERDAY THE BIRD OF NIGHT DID SIT AT NOONDAY UPON THE MARKET-PLACE, HOOTING AND SHRIEKING.
WHEN THESE PRODIGIES MEET, LET NOT MEN SAY, "THEY ARE NATURAL."
I BELIEVE THEY ARE PORTENTOUS THINGS.

INDEED, IT IS A STRANGE-DISPOSED TIME.
BUT MEN MAY CONSTRUE THINGS AFTER THEIR FASHION...
COMES CAESAR TO THE CAPITOL TOMORROW?
HE DID BID ANTONY SEND WORD TO YOU HE WOULD BE THERE TOMORROW.
GOODNIGHT THEN, CASCA. THIS DISTURBED SKY IS NOT TO WALK IN.
FAREWELL, CICERO.

CASSIUS, WHAT NIGHT IS THIS!
A VERY PLEASING NIGHT TO HONEST MEN.
WHO EVER KNEW THE HEAVENS MENACE SO?
I HAVE WALKED ABOUT THE STREETS AND BARED MY BOSOM TO THE THUNDER-STONE.
BUT WHEREFORE DID YOU SO MUCH TEMPT THE HEAVENS?

YOU LOOK PALE TO SEE THE STRANGE IMPATIENCE OF THE HEAVENS.
BUT CONSIDER THE TRUE CAUSE WHY ALL THESE THINGS CHANGE TO MONSTROUS QUALITY...

YOU SHALL FIND THAT HEAVEN HATH INFUSED THEM WITH THESE SPIRITS TO MAKE THEM INSTRUMENTS OF FEAR AND WARNING.
NOW COULD I NAME TO THEE A MAN MOST LIKE THIS DREADFUL NIGHT...
A MAN NO MIGHTIER THAN THYSELF OR ME, YET PRODIGIOUS GROWN.
'TIS CAESAR THAT YOU MEAN, IS IT NOT, CASSIUS?

LET IT BE WHO IT IS.
OUR YOKE AND SUFFERANCE SHOW US WOMANISH.
THEY SAY THE SENATORS TOMORROW MEAN TO ESTABLISH CAESAR AS A KING.
HE SHALL WEAR HIS CROWN BY SEA AND LAND, IN EVERY PLACE, SAVE HERE IN ITALY.
I KNOW WHERE I WILL WEAR THIS DAGGER THEN!
CASSIUS FROM BONDAGE WILL DELIVER CASSIUS.

THAT TYRANNY THAT I DO BEAR I CAN SHAKE OFF AT PLEASURE.
SO CAN I.
AND WHY SHOULD CAESAR BE A TYRANT THEN?
I KNOW HE WOULD NOT BE A WOLF BUT THAT HE SEES THE ROMANS ARE BUT SHEEP.

WHAT TRASH IS ROME TO ILLUMINATE SO VILE A THING AS CAESAR!
YOU SPEAK TO CASCA.
I WILL SET THIS FOOT OF MINE AS FAR AS WHO GOES FURTHEST.
THERE'S A BARGAIN MADE.

I HAVE MOVED ALREADY SOME OF THE NOBLEST-MINDED ROMANS TO UNDERGO WITH ME AN ENTERPRISE OF HONOURABLE-DANGEROUS CONSEQUENCE.

THIS FEARFUL NIGHT FAVOURS THE WORK WE HAVE IN HAND, MOST BLOODY, FIERY, AND MOST TERRIBLE.

HERE COMES ONE IN HASTE.
HE IS A FRIEND. CINNA, WHERE HASTE YOU SO?
TO FIND YOU.
O CASSIUS! IF YOU COULD BUT WIN THE NOBLE BRUTUS TO OUR PARTY –

BE YOU CONTENT.
CINNA, TAKE THIS WHERE BRUTUS MAY FIND IT AT HIS WINDOW.
ALL THIS DONE, REPAIR TO POMPEY'S PORCH, WHERE YOU SHALL FIND US.
METELLUS CIMBER'S GONE TO SEEK YOU AT YOUR HOUSE.
WELL, I WILL HIE...

COME, CASCA, YOU AND I WILL YET ERE DAY SEE BRUTUS AT HIS HOUSE.
THREE PARTS OF HIM IS OURS ALREADY. THE MAN ENTIRE UPON THE NEXT ENCOUNTER YIELDS HIM OURS.
O, HE SITS HIGH IN ALL THE PEOPLE'S HEARTS.
WE WILL AWAKE HIM AND BE SURE OF HIM.

BRUTUS AT DAWN IN HIS HOME
IT MUST BE BY HIS DEATH.
HE WOULD BE CROWNED.
HOW THAT MIGHT CHANGE HIS NATURE, THERE'S THE QUESTION.
IT IS THE BRIGHT DAY THAT BRINGS FORTH THE ADDER.
CROWN HIM—? THEN, I GRANT, WE PUT A STING IN HIM.

TO SPEAK TRUTH OF CAESAR,
I HAVE NOT KNOWN WHEN HIS AFFECTIONS
SWAYED MORE THAN HIS REASON.
BUT THINK HIM AS A SERPENT'S EGG,
WHICH HATCHED WOULD GROW MISCHIEVOUS –
– AND KILL HIM IN THE SHELL.

SIR, I FOUND THIS.
I AM SURE IT DID NOT LIE THERE WHEN I WENT TO BED.
IS NOT TOMORROW THE IDES OF MARCH?
LOOK IN THE CALENDAR AND BRING ME WORD.

BRUTUS, THOU SLEEP'ST. AWAKE AND SEE THYSELF. SPEAK, STRIKE, REDRESS!
SHALL ROME STAND UNDER ONE MAN'S AWE?
AM I ENTREATED TO SPEAK AND STRIKE?
O ROME!
I MAKE THEE PROMISE – THOU RECEIVEST THY FULL PETITION AT THE HAND OF BRUTUS!

SINCE CASSIUS FIRST DID WHET ME AGAINST CAESAR, I HAVE NOT SLEPT.
ALL THE INTERIM IS LIKE A HIDEOUS DREAM.
SIR, 'TIS CASSIUS AT THE DOOR.

IS HE ALONE?
NO, SIR, THERE ARE MORE WITH HIM.
DO YOU KNOW THEM?
NO, SIR, THEIR FACES ARE BURIED IN THEIR CLOAKS.
LET 'EM ENTER.

SHAM'ST THOU TO SHOW THY DANGEROUS BROW BY NIGHT, WHEN EVILS ARE MOST FREE?
O!
THEN BY DAY WHERE WILT THOU FIND A CAVERN DARK ENOUGH TO MASK THY MONSTROUS VISAGE?
THEY ARE THE FACTION.
O CONSPIRACY!
SEEK NONE, CONSPIRACY. HIDE IT IN SMILES AND AFFABILITY.

THE CONSPIRATORS: CASSIUS, CASCA, DECIUS, CINNA, METELLUS CIMBER AND TREBONIUS.
KNOW I THESE MEN THAT COME ALONG WITH YOU?
YES, EVERY MAN OF THEM – AND NO MAN HERE BUT HONOURS YOU.
THIS IS TREBONIUS.
HE IS WELCOME HITHER.

THIS, DECIUS.
CASCA.
THEY ARE ALL WELCOME.
GIVE ME YOUR HANDS, ONE BY ONE.
AND LET US SWEAR OUR RESOLUTION.

AND METELLUS CIMBER.
CINNA.
NO, NOT AN OATH.
WHAT OTHER OATH THAN HONESTY THAT THIS SHALL BE?
DO NOT STAIN THE VIRTUE OF OUR ENTERPRISE TO THINK THAT OUR CAUSE NEED AN OATH.

BUT WHAT OF CICERO?
I THINK HE WILL STAND
STRONG WITH US.
HE WILL NEVER
FOLLOW ANYTHING
THAT OTHER MEN
BEGIN.
THEN LEAVE
HIM OUT.
SHALL NO MAN
ELSE BE TOUCHED BUT
ONLY CAESAR?

I THINK IT IS NOT MEET MARK ANTONY, SO WELL BELOVED OF CAESAR, SHOULD OUTLIVE CAESAR.
WE SHALL FIND HIM A SHREWD CONTRIVER.
LET ANTONY AND CAESAR FALL TOGETHER.
OUR COURSE WILL SEEM TOO BLOODY, CASSIUS, TO CUT THE HEAD OFF AND THEN HACK THE LIMBS.

LET'S BE SACRIFICERS, BUT NOT BUTCHERS.

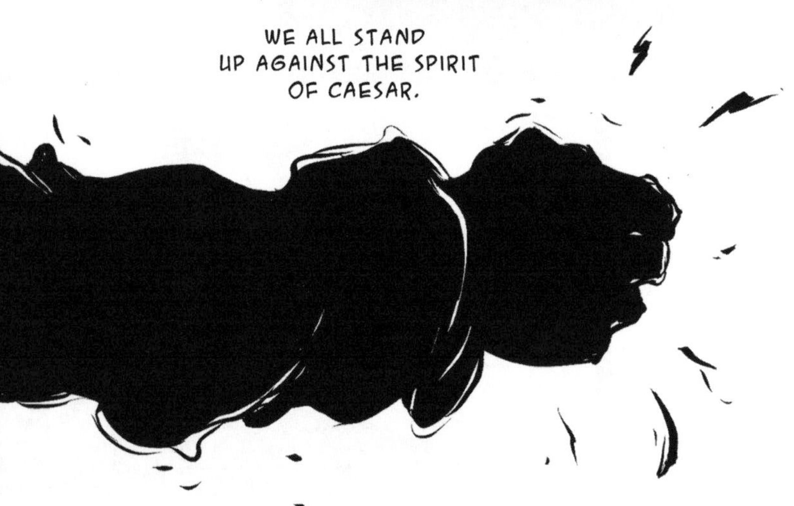
WE ALL STAND UP AGAINST THE SPIRIT OF CAESAR.

LET'S KILL HIM BOLDLY, BUT NOT WRATHFULLY.

TO THE COMMON EYES, WE SHALL BE CALLED PURGERS, NOT MURDERERS.
AND, FOR MARK ANTONY, HE CAN DO NO MORE THAN CAESAR'S ARM WHEN CAESAR'S HEAD IS OFF.
YET I FEAR HIM FOR THE LOVE HE BEARS TO CAESAR...

BUT IT IS DOUBTFUL
WHETHER CAESAR WILL
COME FORTH THIS DAY.
HE IS SUPERSTITIOUS
GROWN OF LATE.
THESE APPARENT PRODIGIES,
THE UNACCUSTOMED TERROR OF
THIS NIGHT, MAY HOLD HIM
FROM THE CAPITOL
TODAY.
NEVER FEAR
THAT.
IF HE BE SO
RESOLVED, I CAN
O'ERSWAY HIM.

I WILL BRING HIM TO THE CAPITOL.
ALBINUS
NAY, WE WILL ALL OF US BE THERE TO FETCH HIM.
BY THE EIGHTH HOUR.
THE MORNING COMES. WE'LL LEAVE YOU, BRUTUS.
FRIENDS, DISPERSE YOURSELVES.

PORTIA, WIFE OF BRUTUS, IS AWOKEN.
BRUTUS, MY LORD!
PORTIA, WHEREFORE RISE YOU NOW?
IT IS NOT FOR YOUR HEALTH THUS TO COMMIT YOUR WEAK CONDITION TO THE RAW COLD MORNING.
IS BRUTUS SICK?
WILL HE STEAL OUT OF HIS WHOLESOME BED TO DARE THE VILE CONTAGION OF THE NIGHT?

YOU HAVE SOME SICK OFFENCE WITHIN YOUR MIND WHICH, BY VIRTUE OF MY PLACE, I OUGHT TO KNOW OF.
WHAT MEN TONIGHT HAVE HAD RESORT TO YOU?
FOR HERE HAVE BEEN SOME SIX OR SEVEN WHO DID HIDE THEIR FACES EVEN FROM DARKNESS.
KNEEL NOT, GENTLE PORTIA.

I SHOULD NOT NEED, IF YOU WERE GENTLE BRUTUS.
SHOULD I KNOW NO SECRETS THAT APPERTAIN TO YOU?
DWELL I BUT IN THE SUBURBS OF YOUR GOOD PLEASURE?
IF IT BE NO MORE, PORTIA IS BRUTUS' HARLOT, NOT HIS WIFE.
YOU ARE MY TRUE AND HONOURABLE WIFE.

IF THIS WERE TRUE, THEN SHOULD I KNOW THIS SECRET.
THINK YOU I AM NO STRONGER THAN MY SEX?
I HAVE MADE STRONG PROOF OF MY CONSTANCY, GIVING MYSELF A VOLUNTARY WOUND HERE, IN THE THIGH.
CAN I BEAR THAT WITH PATIENCE AND NOT MY HUSBAND'S SECRETS?
O YE GODS!
RENDER ME WORTHY OF THIS NOBLE WIFE!

AT THE HOME OF CAESAR AND HIS WIFE CALPURNIA
NOR HEAVEN NOR EARTH HAVE BEEN AT PEACE TONIGHT.
THRICE HATH CALPURNIA IN HER SLEEP CRIED OUT, "HELP, HO! THEY MURDER CAESAR!"
MY LORD!
GO BID THE PRIESTS DO PRESENT SACRIFICE, AND BRING ME THEIR OPINIONS OF SUCCESS.

WHAT MEAN YOU, CAESAR?
YOU SHALL NOT STIR OUT OF YOUR HOUSE TODAY.
THE THINGS THAT THREATENED ME NE'ER LOOKED BUT ON MY BACK.
WHEN THEY SHALL SEE THE FACE OF CAESAR, THEY ARE VANISHED.

CAESAR, I NEVER STOOD ON CEREMONIES, YET NOW THEY FRIGHT ME.
GRAVES HAVE YAWNED AND YIELDED UP THEIR DEAD...

FIERY WARRIORS FOUGHT UPON THE CLOUDS IN RANKS, WHICH DRIZZLED BLOOD UPON THE CAPITOL...
GHOSTS SHRIEK AND SQUEAL ABOUT THE STREETS.

O CAESAR!
THESE THINGS ARE BEYOND ALL USE, AND I DO FEAR THEM.
WHAT CAN BE AVOIDED WHOSE END IS PURPOSED BY THE MIGHTY GODS?
YET CAESAR SHALL GO FORTH.
WHEN BEGGARS DIE, THERE ARE NO COMETS SEEN.
THE HEAVENS THEMSELVES BLAZE FORTH THE DEATH OF PRINCES.

COWARDS DIE MANY TIMES BEFORE THEIR DEATHS.
THE VALIANT NEVER TASTE OF DEATH BUT ONCE.
WHAT SAY THE AUGURERS?
THEY WOULD NOT HAVE YOU STIR FORTH TODAY.
PLUCKING THE ENTRAILS OF AN OFFERING, THEY COULD NOT FIND A HEART WITHIN THE BEAST.

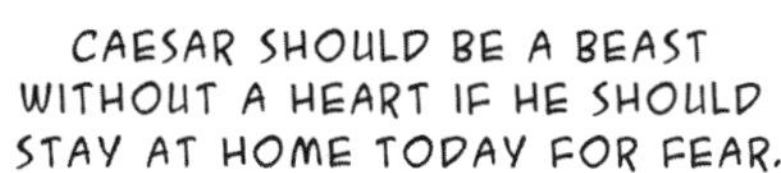
CAESAR SHOULD BE A BEAST
WITHOUT A HEART IF HE SHOULD
STAY AT HOME TODAY FOR FEAR.

DANGER KNOWS FULL
WELL THAT CAESAR IS MORE
DANGEROUS THAN HE.

CAESAR SHALL
GO FORTH.

CALL IT MY FEAR THAT KEEPS YOU IN THE HOUSE AND NOT YOUR OWN.
WE'LL SEND MARK ANTONY TO THE SENATE, AND HE SHALL SAY YOU ARE NOT WELL TODAY.
MARK ANTONY SHALL SAY I AM NOT WELL...
AND, FOR THY HUMOUR, I WILL STAY AT HOME.

HERE'S DECIUS.
CAESAR, ALL HAIL!
I COME TO FETCH YOU TO THE SENATE.
BEAR MY GREETING TO THE SENATORS, AND TELL THEM THAT I WILL NOT COME TODAY.
SAY HE IS SICK.

SHALL CAESAR SEND A LIE?

HAVE I IN CONQUEST STRETCHED MINE ARM SO FAR TO BE AFEARD TO TELL THE TRUTH?

THE CAUSE IS IN MY WILL. I WILL NOT COME.
THAT IS ENOUGH TO SATISFY THE SENATE.
BUT FOR YOUR PRIVATE SATISFACTION, I WILL LET YOU KNOW...
CALPURNIA DREAMT TONIGHT SHE SAW MY STATUE WHICH, LIKE A FOUNTAIN, DID RUN PURE BLOOD.

MANY ROMANS CAME SMILING AND DID BATHE THEIR HANDS IN IT.
AND THESE SHE DOES APPLY FOR WARNINGS AND EVILS IMMINENT.

THIS DREAM IS ALL AMISS INTERPRETED.
YOUR STATUE SPOUTING BLOOD, IN WHICH SO MANY SMILING ROMANS BATHED, SIGNIFIES THAT FROM YOU GREAT ROME SHALL SUCK REVIVING BLOOD. THIS BY CALPURNIA'S DREAM IS SIGNIFIED.
AND THIS WAY HAVE YOU WELL EXPOUNDED IT.

KNOW NOW THE SENATE HAVE CONCLUDED TO GIVE THIS DAY A CROWN TO MIGHTY CAESAR.
IF YOU SEND THEM WORD YOU WILL NOT COME, THEIR MINDS MAY CHANGE.
IF CAESAR HIDE HIMSELF, SHALL THEY NOT WHISPER "LO! CAESAR IS AFRAID"?

HOW FOOLISH DO YOUR FEARS SEEM NOW, CALPURNIA!
LOOK WHERE PUBLIUS IS COME TO FETCH ME.
WHAT, BRUTUS, ARE YOU STIRRED SO EARLY TOO?
GOOD MORROW, CASCA. CAIUS LIGARIUS...

SEE! ANTONY IS UP.
NOW, CINNA, METELLUS, TREBONIUS!
BE NEAR ME, THAT I MAY REMEMBER YOU.
SO NEAR WILL I BE, THAT YOUR BEST FRIENDS SHALL WISH I HAD BEEN FURTHER!
GOOD FRIENDS, WE WILL STRAIGHTWAY GO TOGETHER.

PORTIA SENDS FOR NEWS OF BRUTUS...
I PRITHEE, BOY, RUN TO THE SENATE...
O CONSTANCY...
BE STRONG UPON MY SIDE. SET A HUGE MOUNTAIN BETWEEN MY HEART AND TONGUE.
ART THOU HERE YET?
MADAM, WHAT SHOULD I DO?
RUN TO THE CAPITOL AND NOTHING ELSE?

YES, BRING ME WORD IF THY LORD LOOK WELL, WHAT CAESAR DOTH, WHAT SUITORS PRESS TO HIM.
HARK, BOY!
WHAT NOISE IS THAT?
I HEAR NONE, MADAM.
LISTEN WELL. I HEARD A RUMOUR, LIKE A FRAY. THE WIND BRINGS IT FROM THE CAPITOL.
SOOTH, I HEAR NOTHING.

COME HITHER, FELLOW. IS CAESAR YET GONE TO THE CAPITOL?
I GO TO TAKE MY STAND TO SEE HIM PASS ON TO THE CAPITOL.

WHY, KNOW'ST THOU ANY HARM INTENDED TOWARDS HIM?

NONE THAT I KNOW, MUCH THAT I FEAR.
O BRUTUS...
THE HEAVENS SPEED THEE IN THINE ENTERPRISE!
O, I GROW FAINT.
RUN, LUCIUS, TO MY LORD.
SAY I AM MERRY. BRING ME WORD WHAT HE DOTH SAY TO THEE.

THE IDES OF MARCH ARE COME.
THE CONSPIRATORS CLOSE THE TRAP ON CAESAR.
AY, CAESAR, BUT NOT GONE.
TREBONIUS KNOWS HIS TIME.
LOOK YOU, BRUTUS, HE DRAWS MARK ANTONY OUT OF THE WAY.
WHERE IS METELLUS CIMBER?
LET HIM PREFER HIS SUIT TO CAESAR.
CASCA, YOU ARE THE FIRST THAT REARS YOUR HAND.
PRESS NEAR AND SECOND HIM.

MOST MIGHTY CAESAR, METELLUS CIMBER THROWS BEFORE THY SEAT AN HUMBLE HEART –
THY BROTHER BY DECREE IS BANISHED.
IF THOU DOST BEND AND PRAY AND FAWN FOR HIM, I SPURN THEE LIKE A CUR OUT OF MY WAY.

IS THERE NO VOICE MORE WORTHY THAN MY OWN FOR THE REPEALING OF MY BANISHED BROTHER?
I KISS THY HAND THAT PUBLIUS CIMBER MAY HAVE AN IMMEDIATE FREEDOM OF REPEAL.
WHAT, BRUTUS?
AS LOW AS TO THY FOOT DOTH CASSIUS FALL, TO BEG FOR PUBLIUS CIMBER.

I COULD BE WELL MOVED IF I WERE AS YOU...
BUT I AM CONSTANT AS THE NORTHERN STAR.
MEN ARE FLESH AND BLOOD, AND APPREHENSIVE. YET IN THE NUMBER I DO KNOW BUT ONE THAT UNASSAILABLE HOLDS HIS RANK, AND I AM HE.
I WAS CONSTANT CIMBER SHOULD BE BANISHED, AND CONSTANT DO REMAIN TO KEEP HIM SO.

O CAESAR!
WILT THOU LIFT UP OLYMPUS?
GREAT CAESAR!
DOTH NOT BRUTUS KNEEL?
SPEAK, HANDS, FOR ME!

ET TU,
BRUTE?
THEN FALL,
CAESAR!

LIBERTY!
FREEDOM!
TYRANNY IS DEAD!
CRY OUT LIBERTY! FREEDOM!
PEOPLE AND SENATORS, BE NOT AFFRIGHTED! AMBITION'S DEBT IS PAID.

WHERE IS ANTONY?
FLED TO HIS HOUSE AMAZED.
MEN, WIVES AND CHILDREN STARE, CRY OUT AND RUN AS IT WERE DOOMSDAY.

HE THAT CUTS OFF TWENTY YEARS OF LIFE CUTS OFF SO MANY YEARS OF FEARING DEATH.
SO ARE WE CAESAR'S FRIENDS THAT HAVE ABRIDGED HIS TIME OF FEARING DEATH.
LET US BATHE OUR HANDS IN CAESAR'S BLOOD, AND WAVING OUR RED WEAPONS O'ER OUR HEADS, LET'S ALL CRY, "PEACE, FREEDOM, AND LIBERTY!"

HOW MANY AGES HENCE SHALL THIS LOFTY SCENE BE ACTED OVER!
OFTEN SHALL THE KNOT OF US BE CALLED THE MEN THAT GAVE THEIR COUNTRY LIBERTY.
BUT HERE COMES ANTONY. WELCOME, MARK ANTONY!
O MIGHTY CAESAR! DOST THOU LIE SO LOW?
ARE ALL THY CONQUESTS SHRUNK TO THIS LITTLE MEASURE? FARE THEE WELL.

I KNOW NOT, GENTLEMEN, WHO ELSE MUST BE LET BLOOD.
IF I MYSELF, NO PLACE WILL PLEASE ME SO, NO MEAN OF DEATH, AS HERE BY CAESAR.
O ANTONY, BEG NOT YOUR DEATH OF US.
YOU SEE BUT OUR HANDS AND THIS BLEEDING BUSINESS THEY HAVE DONE...

OUR HEARTS
YOU SEE NOT.
PITY TO THE GENERAL
WRONG OF ROME – PITY – HATH
DONE THIS DEED ON CAESAR.
OUR HEARTS
DO RECEIVE YOU
WITH ALL KIND LOVE
AND REVERENCE.

YOUR VOICE SHALL BE AS STRONG AS ANY MAN'S IN THE DISPOSING OF NEW DIGNITIES.
ONLY BE PATIENT TILL WE HAVE APPEASED THE MULTITUDE.
THEN WE WILL DELIVER YOU THE CAUSE WHY I, THAT DID LOVE CAESAR WHEN I STRUCK HIM, HAVE THUS PROCEEDED.

GENTLEMEN – ALAS! WHAT SHALL I SAY?
THAT I DID LOVE THEE, CAESAR, O 'TIS TRUE!
SHALL IT NOT GRIEVE THEE TO SEE THY ANTONY MAKING HIS PEACE WITH THINE ENEMIES?
PARDON ME, JULIUS!

I BLAME YOU NOT FOR PRAISING CAESAR SO.
BUT WHAT COMPACT MEAN YOU TO HAVE WITH US?
WILL YOU BE IN NUMBER OF OUR FRIENDS, OR SHALL WE NOT DEPEND ON YOU?
FRIENDS AM I WITH YOU ALL, AND LOVE YOU ALL, UPON THIS HOPE THAT YOU SHALL GIVE ME REASONS WHY CAESAR WAS DANGEROUS.

OUR REASONS ARE SO GOOD THAT WERE YOU THE SON OF CAESAR, YOU SHOULD BE SATISFIED.
THAT'S ALL I SEEK...
AND THAT I MAY PRODUCE HIS BODY TO THE MARKET-PLACE, AND SPEAK IN THE ORDER OF HIS FUNERAL.
YOU SHALL, MARK ANTONY.

DO NOT CONSENT THAT ANTONY SPEAK IN HIS FUNERAL.
KNOW YOU HOW MUCH THE PEOPLE MAY BE MOVED BY THAT WHICH HE WILL UTTER?
I WILL MYSELF FIRST SHOW THE REASON OF CAESAR'S DEATH.
I LIKE IT NOT.

MARK ANTONY, TAKE YOU CAESAR'S BODY.
YOU SHALL NOT IN YOUR FUNERAL SPEECH BLAME US, BUT SAY YOU DO IT BY OUR PERMISSION.
YOU SHALL SPEAK AFTER MY SPEECH IS ENDED.
BE IT SO. I DO DESIRE NO MORE.

O PARDON ME, THOU BLEEDING PIECE OF EARTH, THAT I AM MEEK AND GENTLE WITH THESE BUTCHERS!
OVER THY WOUNDS NOW DO I PROPHESY DOMESTIC FURY AND FIERCE CIVIL STRIFE...
AND CAESAR'S SPIRIT, COME HOT FROM HELL, SHALL CRY "HAVOC!" AND LET SLIP THE DOGS OF WAR!

YOU SERVE OCTAVIUS CAESAR, DO YOU NOT?
I DO, MARK ANTONY.
CAESAR DID WRITE FOR HIM TO COME TO ROME.
HE IS COMING.
HERE IS A DANGEROUS ROME FOR OCTAVIUS...
STAY AWHILE TILL I HAVE BORNE THIS CORPSE INTO THE MARKET-PLACE.
THERE SHALL I TRY, IN MY ORATION, HOW THE PEOPLE TAKE THE CRUEL ISSUE OF THESE BLOODY MEN.

WE WILL BE SATISFIED! LET US BE SATISFIED!
THEN FOLLOW ME AND GIVE ME AUDIENCE, FRIENDS.
PUBLIC REASONS SHALL BE RENDERED OF CAESAR'S DEATH.
I WILL HEAR BRUTUS SPEAK.

ROMANS, COUNTRYMEN! HEAR ME FOR MY CAUSE WHY BRUTUS ROSE AGAINST CAESAR.
THIS IS MY ANSWER.
NOT THAT I LOVED CAESAR LESS, BUT THAT I LOVED ROME MORE.
HAD YOU RATHER CAESAR WERE LIVING, AND DIE ALL SLAVES, THAN THAT CAESAR WERE DEAD, TO LIVE ALL FREE MEN?

AS CAESAR WAS VALIANT, I HONOUR HIM; BUT, AS HE WAS AMBITIOUS, I SLEW HIM.
WHO IS HERE SO VILE THAT WILL NOT LOVE HIS COUNTRY?
IF ANY, SPEAK, FOR HIM HAVE I OFFENDED.
NONE, BRUTUS, NONE!

THEN NONE HAVE I OFFENDED.
HERE COMES HIS BODY, MOURNED BY MARK ANTONY, WHO HAD NO HAND IN HIS DEATH.
I HAVE THE SAME DAGGER FOR MYSELF, WHEN IT SHALL PLEASE MY COUNTRY TO NEED MY DEATH.

LIVE, BRUTUS! LIVE!
BRING HIM WITH TRIUMPH HOME!
GIVE HIM A STATUE WITH HIS ANCESTORS!
LET HIM BE CAESAR!

GOOD COUNTRYMEN, FOR MY SAKE, STAY HERE WITH ANTONY, AND GRACE HIS SPEECH WHICH ANTONY, BY OUR PERMISSION, IS ALLOWED TO MAKE.
I DO ENTREAT YOU, NOT A MAN DEPART, SAVE I ALONE, TILL ANTONY HAVE SPOKE.

LET US
HEAR MARK
ANTONY.
THIS CAESAR
WAS A TYRANT.
THAT'S CERTAIN.
WE ARE BLESSED THAT
ROME IS RID OF HIM.
PEACE!
LET US HEAR
WHAT ANTONY
CAN SAY.

FRIENDS, ROMANS, COUNTRYMEN, LEND ME YOUR EARS!
I COME TO BURY CAESAR, NOT TO PRAISE HIM...
THE NOBLE BRUTUS HATH TOLD YOU CAESAR WAS AMBITIOUS.
IF IT WERE SO, IT WAS A GRIEVOUS FAULT, AND GRIEVOUSLY HATH CAESAR ANSWERED IT.

YET YOU ALL DID SEE THAT I THRICE PRESENTED HIM A KINGLY CROWN, WHICH HE DID THRICE REFUSE.
WAS THIS AMBITION?
YET BRUTUS SAYS HE WAS AMBITIOUS AND, SURE, HE IS AN HONOURABLE MAN.

I SPEAK NOT TO DISPROVE WHAT BRUTUS SPOKE, BUT HERE I AM TO SPEAK WHAT I DO KNOW.
YOU ALL DID LOVE HIM ONCE, NOT WITHOUT CAUSE. WHAT CAUSE WITHHOLDS YOU THEN TO MOURN FOR HIM?

METHINKS THERE IS MUCH REASON IN HIS SAYINGS.
IF THOU CONSIDER RIGHTLY OF THE MATTER, CAESAR HAS HAD GREAT WRONG.
HE WOULD NOT TAKE THE CROWN. THEREFORE 'TIS CERTAIN HE WAS NOT AMBITIOUS.

IF I WERE DISPOSED TO STIR YOUR HEARTS AND MINDS TO MUTINY AND RAGE, I SHOULD DO BRUTUS WRONG AND CASSIUS WRONG.
I RATHER CHOOSE TO WRONG THE DEAD, TO WRONG MYSELF, AND YOU, THAN WRONG SUCH HONOURABLE MEN.

BUT HERE'S A PARCHMENT WITH THE SEAL OF CAESAR. 'TIS HIS WILL... WHICH, PARDON ME, I DO NOT MEAN TO READ –
WE'LL HEAR THE WILL! READ IT, MARK ANTONY.
WE WILL HEAR CAESAR'S WILL!

I MUST NOT READ IT.
HEARING THE WILL OF CAESAR WILL INFLAME YOU, IT WILL MAKE YOU MAD.
I FEAR I WRONG THE HONOURABLE MEN WHOSE DAGGERS HAVE STABBED CAESAR...
THEY WERE TRAITORS!
THEY WERE VILLAINS, MURDERERS!

YOU WILL COMPEL ME THEN TO READ THE WILL?
THEN LET ME SHOW YOU HIM THAT MADE THE WILL.
IF YOU HAVE TEARS, PREPARE TO SHED THEM NOW...

LOOK! IN THIS PLACE RAN CASSIUS' DAGGER THROUGH.
SEE WHAT A RENT THE ENVIOUS CASCA MADE.
THROUGH THIS, THE WELL-BELOVED BRUTUS STABBED...
THIS WAS THE UNKINDEST CUT OF ALL.

FOR WHEN THE
NOBLE CAESAR SAW
HIM STAB, THEN BURST
HIS MIGHTY HEART AND
GREAT CAESAR FELL!

O, WHAT A FALL WAS THERE, MY COUNTRYMEN!
O PITEOUS SPECTACLE!
O TRAITORS! VILLAINS!
O MOST BLOODY SIGHT!
WE WILL BE REVENGED!

GOOD FRIENDS, LET ME NOT STIR YOU UP TO SUCH A SUDDEN FLOOD OF MUTINY.
THEY THAT HAVE DONE THIS DEED ARE HONOURABLE.
WHAT PRIVATE GRIEFS THEY HAVE, ALAS, I KNOW NOT! THEY ARE WISE AND HONOURABLE AND WILL, NO DOUBT, WITH REASONS ANSWER YOU.

I COME NOT, FRIENDS, TO STEAL AWAY YOUR HEARTS.
I AM NO ORATOR, AS BRUTUS IS, TO STIR MEN'S BLOOD AND PUT A TONGUE IN EVERY WOUND OF CAESAR THAT SHOULD MOVE THE STONES OF ROME TO RISE AND MUTINY.

WE'LL MUTINY!
WE'LL BURN THE HOUSE OF BRUTUS!
WHY, FRIENDS, WHEREIN HATH CAESAR THUS DESERVED YOUR LOVES?
ALAS, YOU KNOW NOT!
I MUST TELL YOU THEN. YOU HAVE FORGOT THE WILL I TOLD YOU OF.

THE WILL! LET'S HEAR THE WILL!
TO EVERY ROMAN CITIZEN HE GIVES SEVENTY-FIVE DRACHMAS.
NOBLE CAESAR! WE'LL REVENGE HIS DEATH.
MOREOVER, HE HATH LEFT YOU ALL HIS PRIVATE ARBOURS AND NEW-PLANTED ORCHARDS FOR EVER.

HERE WAS A CAESAR! WHEN COMES SUCH ANOTHER?
NEVER, NEVER!
WE'LL BURN HIS BODY IN THE HOLY PLACE AND FIRE THE TRAITORS' HOUSES!
GO FETCH FIRE.
NOW, MISCHIEF, THOU ART AFOOT. TAKE THOU WHAT COURSE THOU WILT!

SIR, OCTAVIUS IS AT CAESAR'S HOUSE.
HE COMES UPON A WISH.
FORTUNE IS MERRY AND IN THIS MOOD WILL GIVE US ANYTHING.
I HEARD HIM SAY BRUTUS AND CASSIUS ARE RID LIKE MADMEN THROUGH THE GATES OF ROME.
BELIKE THEY HAD SOME NOTICE OF THE PEOPLE – HOW I MOVED THEM.
BRING ME TO OCTAVIUS.

MARK ANTONY, OCTAVIUS AND LEPIDUS PLAN THEIR STRATEGY.
THESE MANY THEN SHALL DIE...
YOUR BROTHER TOO MUST DIE. CONSENT YOU, LEPIDUS?
I DO CONSENT, UPON CONDITION PUBLIUS SHALL NOT LIVE, WHO IS YOUR SISTER'S SON, MARK ANTONY.

HE SHALL NOT LIVE.
LEPIDUS, GO TO CAESAR'S HOUSE, FETCH THE WILL HITHER.
SHALL I FIND YOU HERE?
HERE OR AT THE CAPITOL.

THIS IS A SLIGHT UNMERITABLE MAN...
IS IT FIT, THE THREEFOLD WORLD DIVIDED, HE SHOULD STAND ONE OF THE THREE TO SHARE IT?
BUT HE'S A TRIED AND VALIANT SOLDIER.
SO IS MY HORSE, OCTAVIUS, AND IS LEPIDUS BUT SO.

NOW, OCTAVIUS, LISTEN GREAT THINGS.
BRUTUS AND CASSIUS ARE LEVYING POWERS.
THEREFORE LET OUR ALLIANCE BE COMBINED, OUR BEST FRIENDS MADE, AND LET US SIT IN COUNCIL.
WE ARE BAYED ABOUT WITH MANY ENEMIES.
SOME THAT SMILE HAVE IN THEIR HEARTS, I FEAR, MILLIONS OF MISCHIEFS.

CASSIUS PICKS A QUARREL WITH BRUTUS...
MOST NOBLE BROTHER, YOU HAVE DONE ME WRONG.
HOW SHOULD I WRONG A BROTHER?
BRUTUS, THIS SOBER FORM OF YOURS HIDES WRONGS...
SPEAK YOUR GRIEFS SOFTLY.
THE EYES OF BOTH OUR ARMIES HERE SHOULD PERCEIVE NOTHING BUT LOVE FROM US.
LET US NOT WRANGLE.

YOU HAVE CONDEMNED LUCIUS PELLA FOR TAKING BRIBES.
MY LETTERS, PRAYING ON HIS SIDE, WERE SLIGHTED OFF.
CASSIUS, YOU YOURSELF ARE MUCH CONDEMNED TO HAVE AN ITCHING PALM, TO SELL YOUR OFFICES FOR GOLD TO UNDESERVERS.

I AN ITCHING PALM!
REMEMBER THE IDES OF MARCH... DID NOT GREAT JULIUS BLEED FOR JUSTICE'S SAKE?
WHAT! SHALL ONE OF US, THAT STRUCK THE FOREMOST MAN OF ALL THIS WORLD, NOW CONTAMINATE OUR FINGERS WITH BASE BRIBES?
I HAD RATHER BE A DOG THAN SUCH A ROMAN.

YOU FORGET YOURSELF.
I AM A SOLDIER, OLDER IN PRACTICE, ABLER THAN YOURSELF.
I SAY YOU ARE NOT.
HAVE MIND UPON YOUR HEALTH! TEMPT ME NO FURTHER.

HEAR ME, FOR I WILL SPEAK.
O YE GODS! MUST I ENDURE ALL THIS?
AY, MORE! FRET TILL YOUR PROUD HEART BREAK.
YOU SHALL DIGEST THE VENOM OF YOUR SPLEEN, THOUGH IT DO SPLIT YOU.
FROM THIS DAY FORTH, I'LL USE YOU FOR MY MIRTH, MY LAUGHTER.

IS IT COME TO THIS?
YOU SAY YOU ARE A BETTER SOLDIER.
YOU WRONG ME, BRUTUS.
I SAID AN ELDER SOLDIER, NOT A BETTER.
IF YOU DID, I CARE NOT.

DO NOT PRESUME TOO MUCH UPON MY LOVE.
I MAY DO THAT I SHALL BE SORRY FOR.
YOU HAVE DONE THAT YOU SHOULD BE SORRY FOR!
I DID SEND TO YOU FOR CERTAIN SUMS OF GOLD, TO PAY MY LEGIONS, WHICH YOU DENIED ME.
WAS THAT DONE LIKE CASSIUS?

I DENIED YOU NOT.
YOU DID.
I DID NOT.
HE WAS A FOOL THAT BROUGHT MY ANSWER BACK.
A FRIEND SHOULD BEAR HIS FRIEND'S INFIRMITIES...

YOU LOVE ME NOT.
I DO NOT LIKE YOUR FAULTS.
A FRIENDLY EYE COULD NEVER SEE SUCH FAULTS.
A FLATTERER'S WOULD NOT, THOUGH THEY DO APPEAR AS HUGE AS HIGH OLYMPUS.

COME, ANTONY, AND YOUNG OCTAVIUS, COME! REVENGE YOURSELVES ALONE ON CASSIUS, FOR CASSIUS IS AWEARY OF THE WORLD...
THERE IS MY DAGGER, AND HERE MY NAKED BREAST: WITHIN, A HEART RICHER THAN GOLD...

I, THAT DENIED THEE GOLD, WILL GIVE MY HEART.
STRIKE, AS THOU DID AT CAESAR. FOR, I KNOW, THOU LOVED HIM BETTER THAN EVER THOU LOVED CASSIUS.
SHEATHE YOUR DAGGER.
DO WHAT YOU WILL – DISHONOUR SHALL BE HUMOUR.

HATH CASSIUS LIVED TO BE BUT MIRTH AND LAUGHTER TO HIS BRUTUS?
WHEN I SPOKE THAT, I WAS ILL-TEMPERED.
DO YOU CONFESS SO MUCH? GIVE ME YOUR HAND.
AND MY HEART TOO.
O BRUTUS! HAVE NOT YOU LOVE ENOUGH TO BEAR WITH ME WHEN RASH HUMOUR MAKES ME FORGETFUL?

I DID NOT THINK YOU COULD HAVE BEEN SO ANGRY.
O CASSIUS! I AM SICK OF MANY GRIEFS.
OF YOUR PHILOSOPHY YOU MAKE NO USE, IF YOU GIVE PLACE TO ACCIDENTAL EVILS.
NO MAN BEARS SORROW BETTER. PORTIA IS DEAD.

PORTIA!
O INSUPPORTABLE AND TOUCHING LOSS! UPON WHAT SICKNESS?
IMPATIENT OF MY ABSENCE, AND GRIEF THAT YOUNG OCTAVIUS WITH MARK ANTONY HAVE MADE THEMSELVES SO STRONG –
WITH THIS SHE FELL DISTRACT...
AND, HER ATTENDANTS ABSENT, SWALLOWED FIRE.

AND DIED SO?
EVEN SO.
O YE IMMORTAL GODS!
SPEAK NO MORE OF HER.
GIVE ME A BOWL OF WINE. IN THIS I BURY ALL UNKINDNESS.
FILL, LUCIUS, TILL THE WINE O'ERSWELL THE CUP.

MESSALA, A REPUBLICAN OFFICER, ARRIVES.
WELCOME, GOOD MESSALA.
I HAVE HERE RECEIVED LETTERS THAT YOUNG OCTAVIUS AND MARK ANTONY COME DOWN UPON US WITH A MIGHTY POWER TOWARD PHILIPPI.

MYSELF HAVE LETTERS THAT OCTAVIUS, ANTONY AND LEPIDUS HAVE PUT TO DEATH AN HUNDRED SENATORS.
MINE SPEAK OF SEVENTY SENATORS THAT DIED...
CICERO BEING ONE.
CICERO ONE!

HAD YOU
YOUR LETTERS
FROM YOUR WIFE,
MY LORD?
NO, MESSALA.
WELL, TO
OUR WORK ALIVE.
WHAT DO YOU THINK
OF MARCHING TO
PHILIPPI?
I DO
NOT THINK
IT GOOD.

YOUR REASON?
'TIS BETTER THAT THE ENEMY SEEK US.
SO SHALL HE WASTE HIS MEANS, WEARY HIS SOLDIERS, WHILST WE, LYING STILL, ARE FULL OF REST, DEFENCE AND NIMBLENESS.

GOOD REASONS MUST GIVE PLACE TO BETTER.
THE PEOPLE 'TWIXT PHILIPPI AND THIS GROUND DO STAND BUT IN A FORCED AFFECTION, FOR THEY HAVE GRUDGED US CONTRIBUTION.
THE ENEMY, MARCHING ALONG BY THEM, SHALL COME ON REFRESHED, NEW-ADDED AND ENCOURAGED.

FROM WHICH ADVANTAGE SHALL WE CUT HIM OFF, IF AT PHILIPPI WE DO FACE HIM THERE, THESE PEOPLE AT OUR BACK.
HEAR ME, GOOD BROTHER –
UNDER YOUR PARDON...

YOU MUST NOTE THAT THE ENEMY INCREASETH EVERY DAY.
WE, AT THE HEIGHT, ARE READY TO DECLINE.
THERE IS A TIDE IN THE AFFAIRS OF MEN, WHICH, TAKEN AT THE FLOOD, LEADS ON TO FORTUNE.
ON SUCH A FULL SEA ARE WE NOW AFLOAT, AND WE MUST TAKE THE CURRENT WHEN IT SERVES, OR LOSE OUR VENTURES.

AY, MY LORD...
THIS IS A SLEEPY TUNE.
I WILL NOT DO THEE SO MUCH WRONG TO WAKE THEE. GOODNIGHT.

HA!
WHO COMES HERE?
I THINK IT IS THE WEAKNESS OF MINE EYES THAT SHAPES THIS MONSTROUS APPARITION.
SPEAK TO ME WHAT THOU ART.
THY EVIL SPIRIT, BRUTUS.

WHY COM'ST THOU?
TO TELL THEE THOU SHALT SEE ME AT PHILIPPI.
WHY, I WILL SEE THEE AT PHILIPPI THEN.
NOW I HAVE TAKEN HEART THOU VANISHEST...

ILL SPIRIT, I WOULD HOLD MORE TALK WITH THEE!
BOY, LUCIUS!
MY LORD!
DIDST THOU SEE ANYTHING?
NOTHING, MY LORD.
GO TO MY BROTHER CASSIUS. BID HIM SET ON HIS POWERS.

PREPARE YOU, GENERALS!
MARK ANTONY, SHALL WE GIVE SIGN OF BATTLE?
NO, CAESAR, WE WILL ANSWER ON THEIR CHARGE.
THE GENERALS WOULD HAVE SOME WORDS.

WORDS BEFORE BLOWS. IS IT SO, COUNTRYMEN?
NOT THAT WE LOVE WORDS BETTER, AS YOU DO.
GOOD WORDS ARE BETTER THAN BAD STROKES, OCTAVIUS.
IN YOUR BAD STROKES, BRUTUS, YOU GIVE GOOD WORDS.
WITNESS THE HOLE YOU MADE IN CAESAR'S HEART, CRYING "LONG LIVE CAESAR!"

LOOK, I DRAW A SWORD AGAINST CONSPIRATORS!
WHEN THINK YOU THAT THE SWORD GOES UP AGAIN?
NEVER, TILL CAESAR'S THREE-AND-THIRTY WOUNDS BE WELL AVENGED!

I WAS NOT BORN TO DIE ON BRUTUS' SWORD.
O!
IF THOU WERT THE NOBLEST OF THY STRAIN, YOUNG MAN, THOU COULDST NOT DIE MORE HONOURABLE.
COME, ANTONY, AWAY!
IF YOU DARE FIGHT TODAY, COME TO THE FIELD.

BLOW WIND, THE STORM IS UP AND ALL IS ON THE HAZARD!
MESSALA!
WHAT SAYS MY GENERAL?
MESSALA, THIS IS MY BIRTHDAY.
BE THOU MY WITNESS THAT AGAINST MY WILL AM I COMPELLED TO SET UPON ONE BATTLE ALL OUR LIBERTIES.

COMING FROM SARDIS,
ON OUR ENSIGN TWO MIGHTY
EAGLES FELL, AND THERE THEY
PERCHED, GORGING AND FEEDING
FROM OUR SOLDIERS' HANDS.

THIS MORNING ARE THEY GONE, AND IN THEIR STEAD DO RAVENS, CROWS AND KITES FLY O'ER OUR HEADS AND LOOK ON US AS WE WERE SICKLY PREY.
THEIR SHADOWS SEEM A CANOPY MOST FATAL, UNDER WHICH OUR ARMY LIES, READY TO GIVE UP THE GHOST.

BELIEVE NOT SO.
I BUT BELIEVE IT PARTLY...

NOW, MOST NOBLE BRUTUS, THE GODS TODAY STAND FRIENDLY.
BUT LET'S REASON WITH THE WORST THAT MAY BEFALL.
IF WE DO LOSE THIS BATTLE, YOU ARE CONTENTED TO BE LED IN TRIUMPH THROUGH THE STREETS OF ROME?
MUNITION

NO, CASSIUS, NO!
THINK NOT THAT EVER BRUTUS
WILL GO BOUND TO ROME.
HE BEARS
TOO GREAT
A MIND.
THIS SAME DAY
MUST END THAT WORK
THE IDES OF MARCH
BEGUN.

WHETHER
WE SHALL MEET AGAIN
I KNOW NOT.
THEREFORE
OUR EVERLASTING
FAREWELL, CASSIUS!
FOR EVER AND
FOR EVER FAREWELL,
BRUTUS!

WHY THEN, LEAD ON!
O, THAT A MAN MIGHT KNOW THE END OF THIS DAY'S BUSINESS!
BUT IT SUFFICETH THAT THE DAY WILL END, AND THEN THE END IS KNOWN.

RIDE, MESSALA, UNTO THE LEGIONS ON THE OTHER SIDE.
LET THEM SET ON AT ONCE, FOR I PERCEIVE A SUDDEN PUSH GIVES THEM THE OVERTHROW.
FOR PORTIA

RIDE, MESSALA: LET THEM ALL COME DOWN!

CASSIUS MEETS HIS OFFICER TITINIUS ON THE BATTLEFIELD
O LOOK, TITINIUS, LOOK, THE VILLAINS FLY!
THIS ENSIGN HERE OF MINE WAS TURNING BACK...
I SLEW THE COWARD AND DID TAKE IT FROM HIM.

O CASSIUS!
BRUTUS GAVE THE WORD TOO EARLY, WHO, HAVING SOME ADVANTAGE ON OCTAVIUS, TOOK IT TOO EAGERLY.
HIS SOLDIERS FELL TO SPOIL, WHILST WE BY ANTONY ARE ALL ENCLOSED.

PINDARUS, SERVANT OF CASSIUS, BRINGS NEWS...
MARK ANTONY IS IN YOUR TENTS, MY LORD!
FLY, THEREFORE, NOBLE CASSIUS, FLY FAR OFF.
THIS HILL IS FAR ENOUGH.
LOOK, TITINIUS, ARE THOSE MY TENTS WHERE I PERCEIVE THE FIRE?
THEY ARE, MY LORD.

TITINIUS, IF THOU LOV'ST ME, MOUNT THOU UP TO YONDER TROOPS THAT I MAY REST ASSURED WHETHER FRIEND OR ENEMY.
I WILL BE HERE AGAIN EVEN WITH A THOUGHT.

GO, PINDARUS, GET HIGHER ON THAT HILL.
REGARD TITINIUS, AND TELL ME WHAT THOU NOT'ST ABOUT THE FIELD.

THIS DAY
I BREATHED
FIRST.
TIME IS
COME ROUND,
AND WHERE I DID BEGIN,
THERE SHALL I END.
MY
LIFE IS RUN HIS
COMPASS.

WHAT NEWS?
TITINIUS IS ENCLOSED ROUND ABOUT...
HE'S TAKEN!
THEY SHOUT FOR JOY.
O, COWARD THAT I AM, TO LIVE SO LONG, TO SEE MY BEST FRIEND TAKEN BEFORE MY FACE!

IN PARTHIA DID I TAKE THEE PRISONER.
AND THEN I SWORE THEE, THAT WHATSOEVER I DID BID THEE DO, THOU SHOULDST ATTEMPT IT.
COME NOW, KEEP THINE OATH.

NOW BE A FREE MAN AND WITH THIS GOOD SWORD, THAT RAN THROUGH CAESAR'S BOWELS, SEARCH THIS BOSOM.
HERE, TAKE THE HILT...
WHEN MY FACE IS COVERED, GUIDE THOU THE SWORD.
CAESAR, THOU ART REVENGED, EVEN WITH THE SWORD THAT KILLED THEE.

SO, I AM FREE, YET WOULD NOT SO HAVE BEEN.
O CASSIUS!
FAR FROM THIS COUNTRY PINDARUS SHALL RUN.

MESSALA GREETS TITINIUS WITH NEWS.
OCTAVIUS IS OVERTHROWN BY NOBLE BRUTUS' POWER, AS CASSIUS' LEGIONS ARE BY ANTONY.
THESE TIDINGS WILL WELL COMFORT CASSIUS.
WHERE DID YOU LEAVE HIM?
IS NOT THAT HE THAT LIES UPON THE GROUND?

NO, THIS WAS HE, MESSALA, BUT CASSIUS IS NO MORE.
MISTRUST OF MY SUCCESS HATH DONE THIS DEED.
O, HATEFUL ERROR!
I GO TO MEET THE NOBLE BRUTUS.
PIERCING STEEL SHALL BE AS WELCOME TO THE EARS OF BRUTUS AS TIDINGS OF THIS SIGHT.

WHY DIDST THOU SEND ME FORTH, BRAVE CASSIUS?
DID I NOT MEET THY FRIENDS?
DID NOT THEY PUT ON MY BROWS THIS WREATH OF VICTORY?
DIDST THOU NOT HEAR THEIR SHOUTS?
ALAS!
THOU HAST MISCONSTRUED EVERYTHING.

BUT TAKE THIS GARLAND ON THY BROW. THY BRUTUS BID ME GIVE IT THEE.
SEE HOW I REGARDED CASSIUS...
COME, CASSIUS' SWORD, AND FIND TITINIUS' HEART.

BRUTUS ARRIVES WITH MESSALA, CATO AND OTHER OFFICERS.
WHERE, MESSALA, DOTH HIS BODY LIE?
LO, YONDER: AND TITINIUS MOURNING IT.
HE IS SLAIN.
O JULIUS CAESAR! THOU ART MIGHTY YET!
THY SPIRIT WALKS ABROAD AND TURNS OUR SWORDS IN OUR OWN ENTRAILS.

BRAVE TITINIUS!
LOOK: HE CROWNED DEAD CASSIUS!
THE LAST OF ALL THE ROMANS, FARE THEE WELL!
COME... LET US TO THE FIELD.
WE SHALL TRY FORTUNE IN A SECOND FIGHT.

A SOLDIER BRINGS A HIGH-RANKING PRISONER TO ANTONY.
BRUTUS IS TAKEN, MY LORD.
WHERE IS HE?
SAFE, ANTONY!
NO ENEMY SHALL EVER TAKE ALIVE THE NOBLE BRUTUS.
THIS IS NOT BRUTUS, BUT A PRIZE NO LESS IN WORTH.

KEEP THIS MAN SAFE.
I HAD RATHER HAVE SUCH MEN MY FRIENDS THAN ENEMIES.
GO ON, SEE WHETHER BRUTUS BE ALIVE OR DEAD, AND BRING US WORD.

MEANWHILE, BRUTUS HIMSELF INSTRUCTS HIS MEN TO ESCAPE...
THE GHOST OF CAESAR HATH APPEARED TO ME TWO TIMES BY NIGHT.
I KNOW MY HOUR IS COME.
NOT SO, MY LORD.
NAY, I AM SURE IT IS.

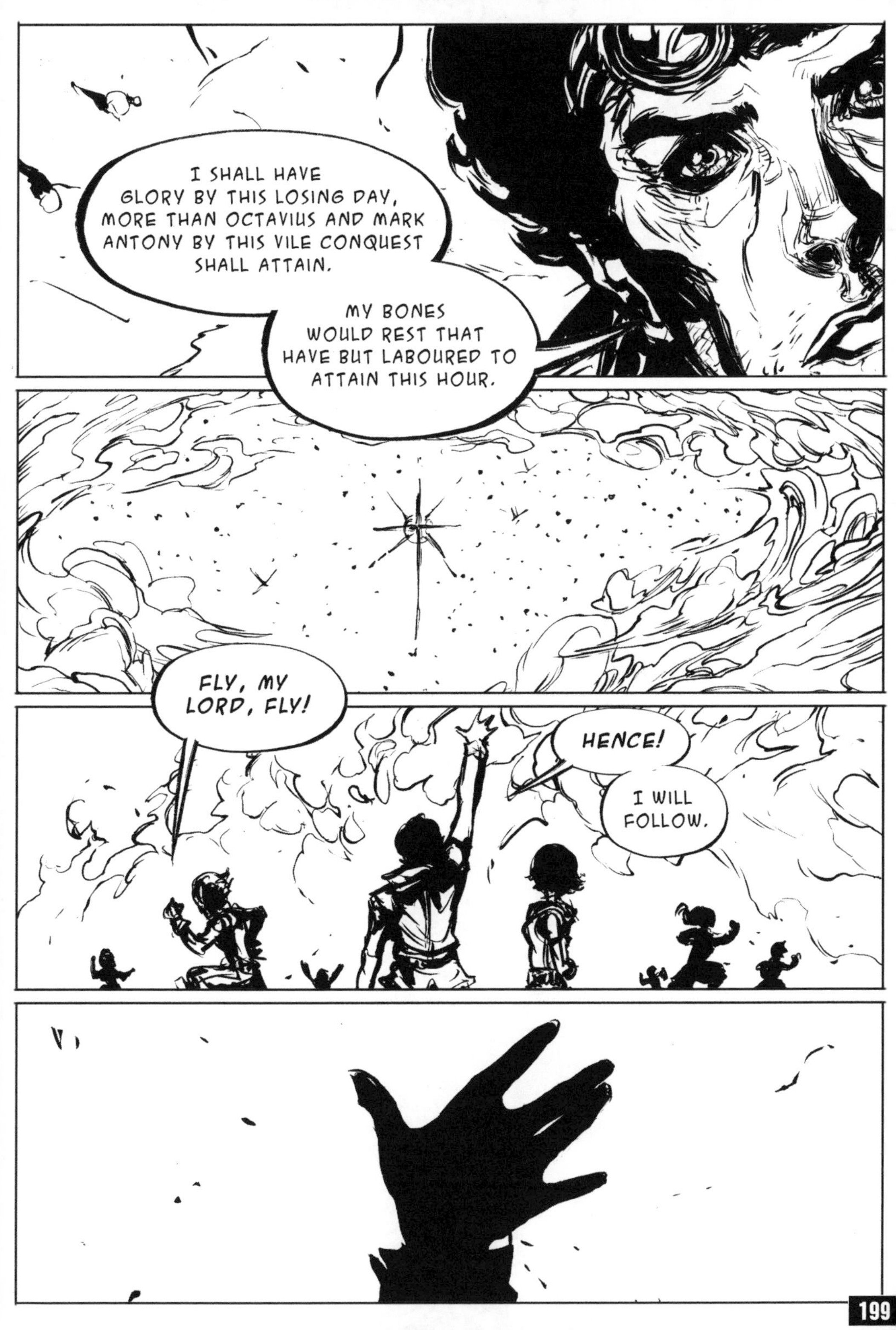
I SHALL HAVE GLORY BY THIS LOSING DAY, MORE THAN OCTAVIUS AND MARK ANTONY BY THIS VILE CONQUEST SHALL ATTAIN.
MY BONES WOULD REST THAT HAVE BUT LABOURED TO ATTAIN THIS HOUR.
FLY, MY LORD, FLY!
HENCE!
I WILL FOLLOW.

I PRITHEE, STRATO, STAY THOU BY THY LORD...
HOLD MY SWORD, AND TURN AWAY THY FACE, WHILE I DO RUN UPON IT.
FARE YOU WELL, MY LORD.
FAREWELL, GOOD STRATO.

CAESAR, NOW BE STILL.
I KILLED NOT THEE WITH HALF SO GOOD A WILL.

MESSALA LEADS ANTONY AND OCTAVIUS TO BRUTUS...
STRATO, WHERE IS THY MASTER?
FREE FROM THE BONDAGE YOU ARE IN, MESSALA.
THE CONQUERORS CAN BUT MAKE A FIRE OF HIM, FOR BRUTUS ONLY OVERCAME HIMSELF, AND NO MAN ELSE HATH HONOUR BY HIS DEATH.

THIS WAS THE NOBLEST ROMAN OF THEM ALL.
ALL THE CONSPIRATORS SAVE ONLY HE DID THAT THEY DID IN ENVY OF GREAT CAESAR.
HE ONLY, IN HONEST THOUGHT AND COMMON GOOD TO ALL, MADE ONE OF THEM.

HIS LIFE WAS GENTLE, AND THE ELEMENTS SO MIXED IN HIM THAT NATURE MIGHT STAND UP AND SAY TO ALL THE WORLD, "THIS WAS A MAN!"
ACCORDING TO HIS VIRTUE LET US USE HIM, WITH ALL RESPECT AND RITES OF BURIAL.
WITHIN MY TENT HIS BONES TONIGHT SHALL LIE, MOST LIKE A SOLDIER, ORDERED HONOURABLY.
SO, CALL THE FIELD TO REST, AND LET'S AWAY TO PART THE GLORIES OF THIS HAPPY DAY.

PLOT SUMMARY OF JULIUS CAESAR

Julius Caesar returns to Rome, a triumphant conqueror, with ambitions to rule as monarch. Cassius and Brutus, veteran republican generals, hear the cries of the mob eager for Caesar's rule. Cassius, jealous of Caesar's success, strives to persuade the idealist Brutus that killing Caesar is the only remedy against tyranny.

A terrifying storm, filled with supernatural portents, occurs that night as Cassius, Casca and Cinna plot against Caesar. The conspirators meet at Brutus's house and convince him to join in their assassination of Caesar the next day.

Portia, wife of Brutus, awakes and seeks to discover the secret that troubles him. Calpurnia, Caesar's wife, also awakes, alerted by nightmares and premonitions of the danger facing him, and pleads with him to stay home. But on that fatal day, the Ides of March, Caesar enters the Senate and is stabbed to death by the conspirators.

Mark Antony, Caesar's loyal general, initially pledges his allegiance to the conspirators, but his speech over Caesar's corpse in the market-place cleverly incites the crowd to vengeful riot. Antony allies himself with Caesar's nephew and heir, Octavius, and their armies prepare to clash with those of Cassius and Brutus at Philippi. Meanwhile, Brutus learns that his wife Portia has committed suicide.

Brutus orders what seems to Cassius a rash assault on Octavius and, in mistaken belief of defeat, Cassius kills himself. The battle eventually turns against Brutus and he too, rather than surrender himself, commits suicide. The victory belongs to Antony and Octavius, who nevertheless praise Brutus for the purity of his motives.

A BRIEF LIFE OF WILLIAM SHAKESPEARE

Shakespeare's birthday is traditionally said to be the 23rd of April – St George's Day, patron saint of England. A good start for England's greatest writer. But that date and even his name are uncertain. He signed his own name in different ways. "Shakespeare" is now the accepted one out of dozens of different versions.

He was born at Stratford-upon-Avon in 1564, and baptized on 26th April. His mother, Mary Arden, was the daughter of a prosperous farmer. His father, John Shakespeare, a glove-maker, was a respected civic figure – and probably also a Catholic. In 1570, just as Will began school, his father was accused of illegal dealings. The family fell into debt and disrepute.

Will attended a local school for eight years. He did not go to university. The next ten years are a blank filled by suppositions. Was he briefly a Latin teacher, a soldier, a sea-faring explorer? Was he prosecuted and whipped for poaching deer?

We do know that in 1582 he married Anne Hathaway, eight years his senior, and three months pregnant. Two more children – twins – were born three years later but, by around 1590, Will had left Stratford to pursue a theatre career in London. Shakespeare's apprenticeship began as an actor and "pen for hire".

He learned his craft the hard way. He soon won fame as a playwright with often-staged popular hits.

He and his colleagues formed a stage company, the Lord Chamberlain's Men, which built the famous Globe Theatre. It opened in 1599 but was destroyed by fire in 1613 during a performance of *Henry VIII* which used gunpowder special effects. It was rebuilt in brick the following year.

Shakespeare was a financially successful writer who invested his money wisely in property. In 1597, he bought an enormous house in Stratford, and in 1608 became a shareholder in London's Blackfriars Theatre. He also redeemed the family's honour by acquiring a personal coat of arms.

Shakespeare wrote over 40 works, including poems, "lost" plays and collaborations, in a career spanning nearly 25 years. He retired to Stratford in 1613, where he died on 23rd April 1616, aged 52, apparently of a fever after a "merry meeting" of drinks with friends. Shakespeare did in fact die on St George's Day! He was buried "full 17 foot deep" in Holy Trinity Church, Stratford, and left an epitaph cursing anyone who dared disturb his bones.

There have been preposterous theories disputing Shakespeare's authorship. Some claim that Sir Francis Bacon (1561–1626), philosopher and Lord Chancellor, was the real author of Shakespeare's plays. Others propose Edward de Vere, Earl of Oxford (1550–1604), or, even more weirdly, Queen Elizabeth I. The implication is that the "real" Shakespeare had to be a university graduate or an aristocrat. Nothing less would do for the world's greatest writer.

Shakespeare is mysteriously hidden behind his work. His life will not tell us what inspired his genius.

EDITORIAL

Richard Appignanesi: Text Adaptor

Richard Appignanesi was a founder and co-director of the Writers & Readers Publishing Cooperative and Icon Books where he originated the internationally acclaimed *Introducing* series. His own best-selling titles in the series include *Freud*, *Postmodernism* and *Existentialism*. He is also the author of the fiction trilogy *Italia Perversa* and the novel *Yukio Mishima's Report to the Emperor*. Currently associate editor of the journal *Third Text* and reviews editor of the journal *Futures*, his latest book *What do Existentialists Believe?* was released in 2006.

Nick de Somogyi: Textual Consultant

Nick de Somogyi works as a freelance writer and researcher, as a genealogist at the College of Arms, and as a contributing editor to *New Theatre Quarterly*. He is the founding editor of the Globe Quartos series, and was the visiting curator at Shakespeare's Globe, 2003–6. His publications include *Shakespeare's Theatre of War* (1998), *Jokermen and Thieves: Bob Dylan and the Ballad Tradition* (1986), and (from 2001) the *Shakespeare Folios* series for Nick Hern Books. He has also contributed to the Open University (1995), Carlton Television (2000), and BBC Radio 3 and Radio 4.

ARTIST

Mustashrik

Mustashrik is an artist, designer and aspiring filmmaker. Born in 1985 in Bangladesh, he came to the UK at a young age. After gaining a Distinction in his Art Foundation, he went on to graduate in Graphic Design (BA Hons) at The University College for The Creative Arts, Epsom.

In 2005, a manga story of his was published in *NEO* Magazine. His work has also appeared in *The Mammoth Book of Best New Manga 2* and in the *D&AD Student Design Awards Annual 2007*, for his entry into the Book Cover Illustration category.

PUBLISHER

SelfMadeHero is a UK-based manga and graphic novel imprint, reinventing some of the most important works of European and world literature.

ALSO IN THE SERIES

RICHARD III
ROMEO & JULIET
THE TEMPEST
HAMLET
MACBETH
A MIDSUMMER NIGHT'S DREAM

www.selfmadehero.com